Name: _____

Form: _____

Coastal Processes and Landforms

- Read, engage and learn!

- Full colour, illustrated Topic Booklet.

- Glossary, Memory Map, Active Learning Game & Flashcards.

- Ideal for ISEB 13+ Common Entrance and KS3 pupils.

Endorsed by:

ISEB Independent Schools Examinations Board

This Oaka™ Books Write Your Own Notes Booklet goes hand in hand with the Active Learning Pack on this topic. The pack includes a Topic Booklet, an Active Learning Game and Question & Answer Flashcards.

Fresh Focus on Learning

Coastal Processes and Landform Glossary

Abrasion: ....
....
....
....

Attrition: ....
....
....
....

Backwash: ....
....
....
....

Bar: ....
....
....
....

Bay: ....
....
....

Beach Nourishment: ....
....
....
....

Coastal Zone: ....
....
....
....

Conflict: ....
....
....

Constructive Waves: ....
....
....
....
....

Corrosion: ....
....
....
....

Deposition: ....
....
....
....

Destructive Waves: ....
....
....
....

Erosion: ....
....
....

Fetch: ....
....
....
....

Groynes: ....
....
....
....

Hard Engineering: ....
....
....
....

Coastal Processes and Landform Glossary

Headland: ....

Soft Engineering: ....

Hydraulic Action: ....

Spit: ....

Longshore Drift: ....

Swash: ....

Managed Retreat: ....

Tombolo: ....

Rip Rap: ....

Transportation: ....

Salt Marshes: ....

Weathering: ....

Sea Wall: ....

Stewardship: ....

1 Coasts and the Coastal Zone

Coasts are shaped by the sea and by ....

- The coast is where land meets the sea.

- The .... is a thin strip between land and sea.

- This strip is being changed by .... and .... all the time.

Sea

Coastal Zone

Land

2 Types of Coastal Area Include...

- beaches, (pebbles/rock/sand)
- sand dunes
- ....
- ....
- natural harbours
- seaside resorts

3 Key Processes

The UK has about ....,........ km of coastline!

3 key processes affect the coast:

- ...., the 'wearing away' of material

- ...., the movement of material up, down and along the coast

- ...., the dropping of .... material.

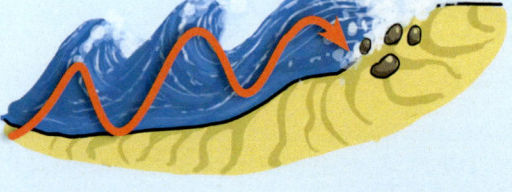

4 **Rock Type**

- .... rock, like limestone, forms steep ....

- .... rock, like clay, forms ....

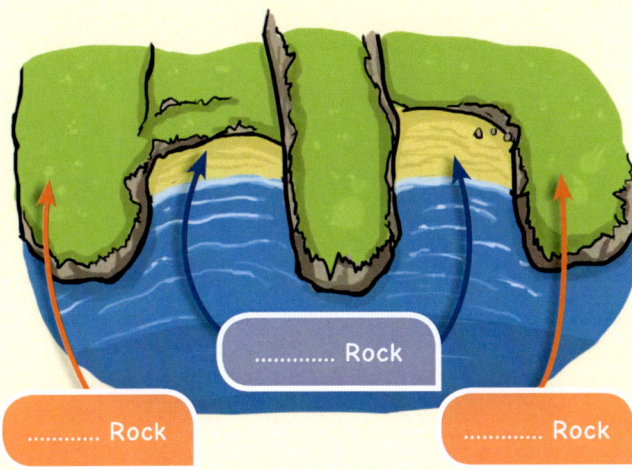

.... Rock

.... Rock

.... Rock

5 **Rock Structure**

- Where the rocks are at an .... to the coast, they will .... at .... rates.

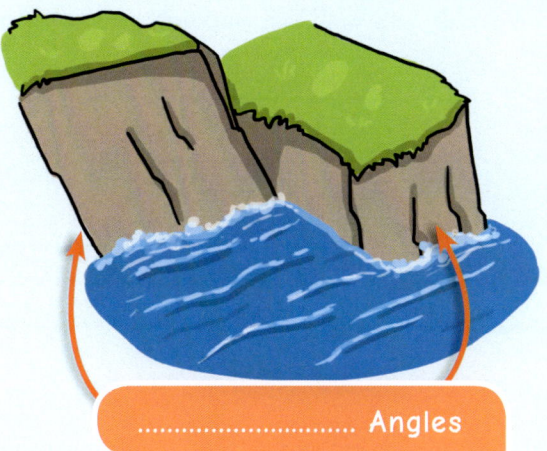

.... Angles

6 **Shape of the coast**

- .... are exposed.

- .... are sheltered so they .... more slowly.

- Bays often include some .... forming a beach.

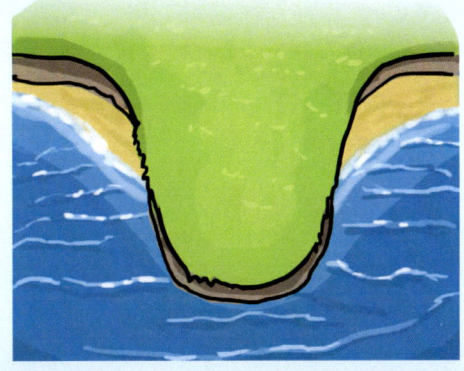

7 **Waves**

- Waves have a huge impact on the ....

- They are created by .... blowing over the sea.

8 Friction on Water

- The .... of the wind on the sea's surface creates ....

- This .... makes water particles .... and the wave moves forward.

9 Wave Size and Energy

- Is affected by the .... of the wind.

- How .... it has been blowing.

- How far the wave has travelled (..........).

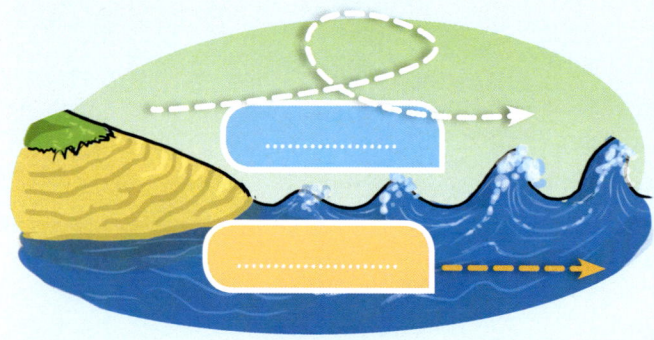

10 How Waves Work

- When a wave breaks, water is washed ..... the beach.

- This is called the ....

- The wave then moves .... the beach.

- This is called the ....

11 Waves Can Be...

.....................:
- these erode.

.........................:
- these deposit and build.

12 .... Waves

- are usually big (great for surfers!)

- have a long ....

- have strong ....

- have weak swash

- are high and steep

- they ....

.... Swash

.... Backwash

13 .... Waves

- are less powerful

- form in .... weather

- have a strong ....

- and a weak ....

- are lower in ....

- .... material.

Strong ....

Deposited Material

Weak ....

14 Coastal Erosion

- The .... and .... of rock along coasts.

15 Destructive Waves

Destructive waves erode by:

- ....

- A............

- A............

- C............... (and Solution)

16 Hydraulic Action

- Water or .... can be .... in joints and cracks in a cliff.

- A wave breaks and .... this air.

- The cliff is .... and ....

- A .... is formed.

.... erodes

- .... compresses the trapped air in the cave.

- This blasts away at the .... of the cave.

- A .... may be formed.

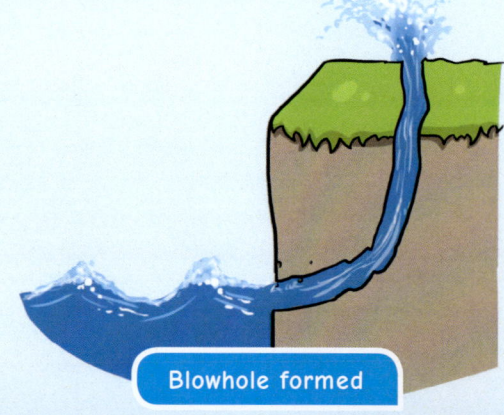

Blowhole formed

17 ....

- Waves throw .... and .... against the cliff.

- This causes damage and .... In storms, big rocks cause more damage.

Sand and pebbles crash against rocks

18 ....

- Waves smash .... and .... into each other.

Current

.... and ...... smash together

19 ....

- The rocks and pebbles break and become ....

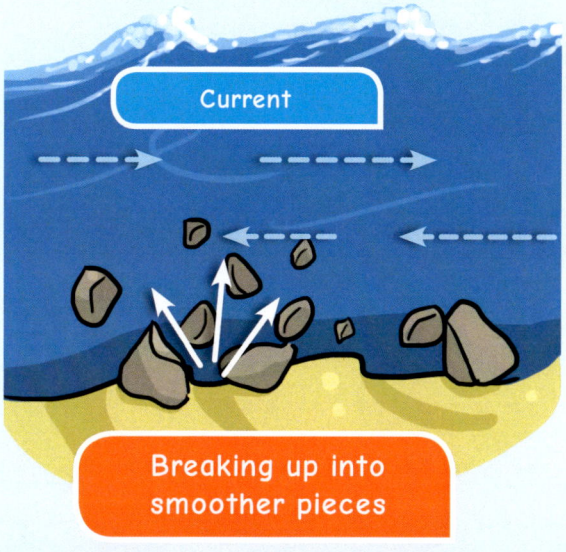

Current

Breaking up into smoother pieces

20 ....

- Weak .... in sea water dissolves some rocks (e.g. .... and **chalk**).

- These are carried away in ....

Cliff erodes

Weak acid in sea water

21

Cliffs

Weather .... the top of the cliff.

The ..... cuts into the .... of the cliff (.............).

The cliff .... and ....

22

H............. and Bays

- .... **rocks**, like **clay** and sand, erode faster than .... rocks, like chalk.

- Where rock is in bands of ..../........../.........., the .... rock sticks out as a ....

- The soft rock erodes, forming ....

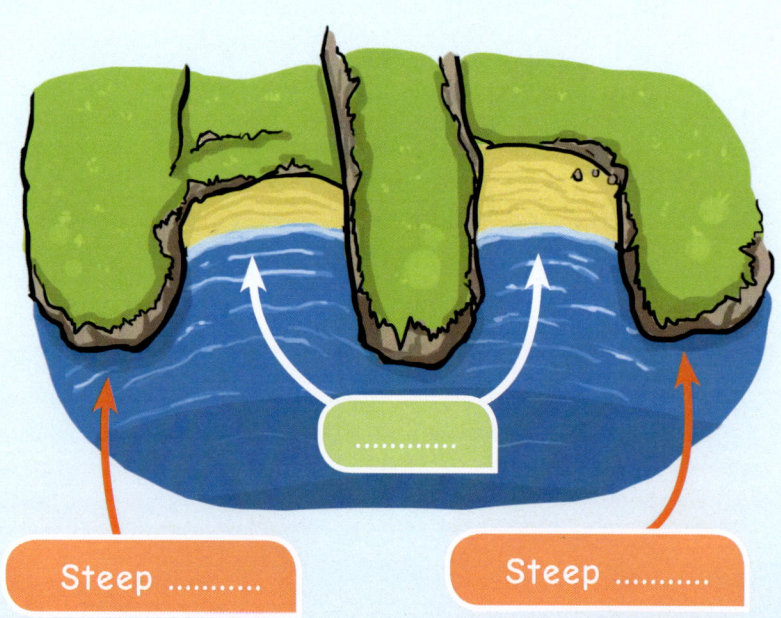

....

Steep ....   Steep ....

Fill in the blanks using these words to help you...

arch   headland   collapses   wears   hydraulic action   arch
pinnacle   pinnacle   wear   cave   stack   stump   waves
disappear   cave   eroded   headland

23 — Cave

- Caves form when .... are pushed into a .... in the rock.

- The .... wears away the rock until a .... is made.

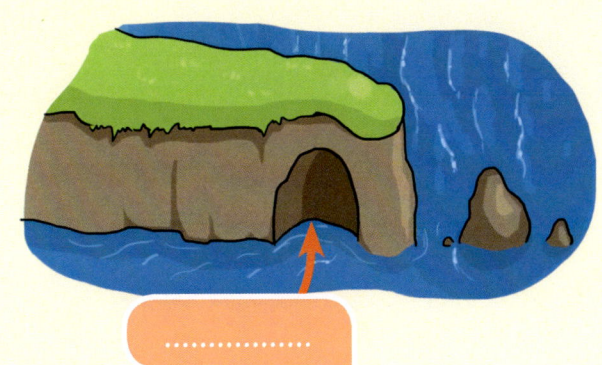

....

24 — Arch

- If the cave is in a ...., it can .... right through the rock to form an ....

Cave ....
through rock

25 — ....

- The .... becomes too big to support the top.

- The top ....

- This leaves a stack, which is separate from the ....

- The stack is weathered and ....

- It gets smaller and then becomes a ....

- Over time, the stump will ....

Collapses

Leaves a stack

26   Formation of Beaches

- Beaches are formed by ....

- This is the .... of .... material by the water.

.... material

27   Deposition

Deposition will happen when...

- waves enter .... water or

- waves enter a .... bay or

- it is ...., with little ....

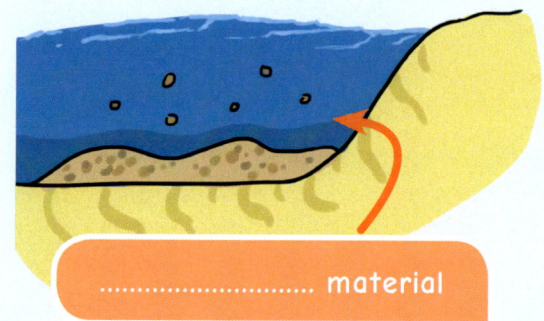

.... material

28   Longshore Drift

- Longshore Drift moves .... material .... the coast.

- It can change the .... of the .... every day!

29   How Longshore Drift Works

- Waves approach the coast at an ....

- .... carries material up the beach at an ....

.... carries material up the beach

30 Zig Zag Movement

- .... carries material back at a .... angle.

- The zig-zag carries .... along.

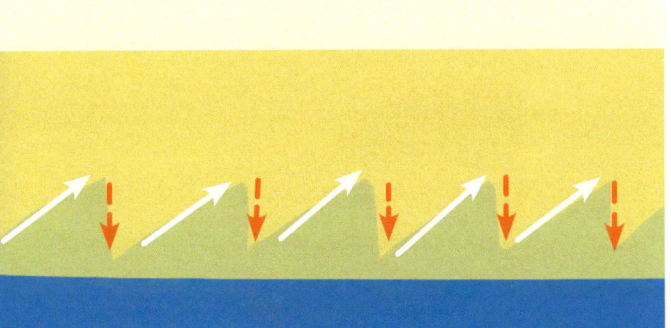

31 Beaches

- Beaches are formed by .... Constructive waves help .... beaches.

- Material on a beach varies in size as you move .... from the ....

Size varies further away from the shoreline

32 Shape of Beaches

- The shape of the beach is called the ....

- Sandy beaches slope ....

Gentle Slope

33 Shingle and Pebbles

- Shingle and .... beaches are ....

Steep Slope

34   Spit

- Spits are caused by ....
- They are ...., ... stretches of beach material.
- They can be found **across a** .... or where the coast changes ....
- .... to the land at one end.
- Caused by ....
- Follow the **direction** of the .... wind.

- Behind a spit water slows down.
- Deposition here may form a salt marsh.

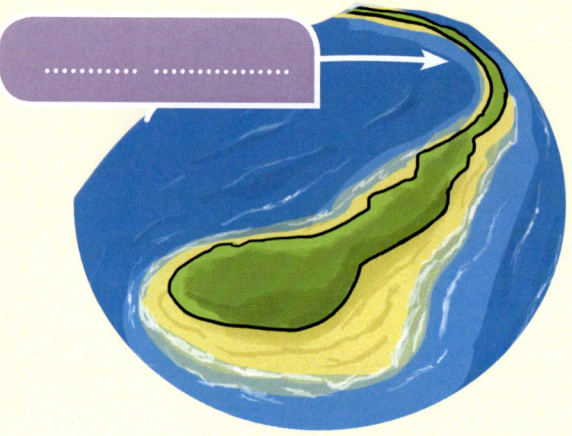
....

35   Bar

- A thin .... of sand and shingle spreads across a bay.
- Formed by ....

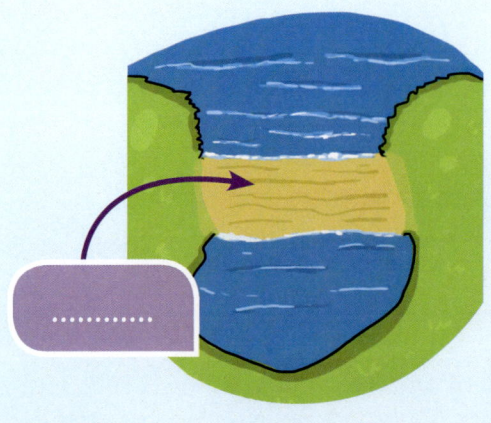
....

36   Tombolo

- Is a .... connecting an .... to the ....

An example is **Chesil Beach.**

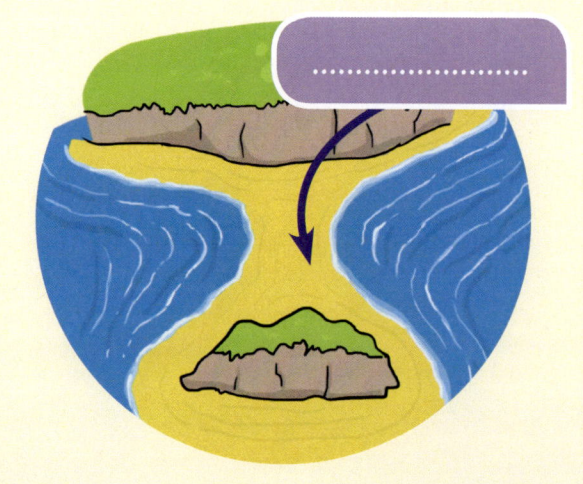
....

37   ....

Form behind spits where there is:

- more s............
- less water ....
- more d....................
- important .... habitats.

38   Living and Working

Coasts are important for lots of reasons and lots of people:

- Places to ....

- River estuaries are important for heavy .... and .... ports.

39   Tourism

- Places to ...., (holidays and ....
- Beautiful ....

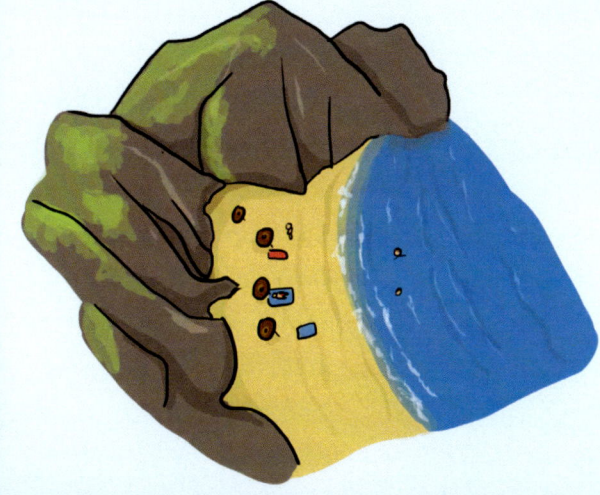

40   Habitats

- Wildlife ....

- ....

41 Coastal Management

There are 2 main types of management:

• ....

• ....

42 ....

Involves building structures to protect the coast.

Structures such as...

• ....

• ....

• ....

43 Positives and Negatives of Sea Walls

+ ....

+ ....

- ....

- ....

- ....
....

44 Positives and Negatives of Groynes

+ ....

+ ....

- ....
....

- ....

Flood Management

45 — Positives and Negatives of Rip Rap

\+ ....

\- ....
....

\- ....

46 — Soft Engineering

• What is meant by 'soft engineering'?

....
....
....
....

47 — Positives and Negatives of Beach Nourishment

\+ ....
\+ ....

\- ....

48 — Positives and Negatives of Managed Retreat

Land becomes marsh.

\+ ....
\+ ....

\- ....

49 Conflicts In Managing Coasts

- **Different groups** want different things.

Save our houses!!

Save our wildlife!!

Save our farmland!!

Help our business!!

50 Groups With An Interest

Groups with an interest include:

- people who .... by the coast
- people who .... there
- ....
- ....

51 Groups With An Interest

- **Councils**

  Need ....

- **Tourist boards**

  Need to attract ....

- **National parks**

  Need to ....the countryside

- **Industry**

  Needs .... routes

52 Why Is There Conflict?

- A person who .... by the coast may want to be **protected** from ....

- .... may not want **ugly engineering**.

Visit our Beaches

53 Conflict

- .... may want to **protect land** they want to .... **on.**

- **Environmentalists** don't want the .... **spoiled.**

Don't spoil the ....!!

54 Conflict

- **National parks** may want ....

- .... will not want to **lose land.**

55 Stewardship

- Coasts need **protecting but** people need to talk to get the **best result** for everyone.

- **Stewardship** is.......................
....
....
....

- We are all responsible for .... our coasts.

Meeting to discuss how to work together.

Fresh Focus on Learning

About Oaka Books

Children learn best when they are engaged...

Our aim is to help children enjoy learning by making it fun! That way they will succeed.

This topic pack follows the Common Entrance syllabus and National Curriculum guidelines for KS3.

The design and layout of our books follow guidelines from the British Dyslexia Association.

ISBN 978-1-911189-69-5

CE/KS3 Ge-
Coastal Erosion

Write Your Own Notes Booklet

9 781911 189695

Three Easy Steps

Read: the easy to follow bullet point Topic Booklet.

Engage: Play the Active Learning Game.

Learn: When you understand the topic, test yourself using the Write Your Own Notes Book. You can use the Topic Booklet to help if you get stuck.

One (short) Topic at a time:

For some students, a big book is a big turn off. That's why we focus on one topic at a time. Short and to the point.

Reading Age

This booklet is suitable for children with a reading age of 10 ½ years.

Topic Packs for KS1, KS2 & KS3 Include:

History
Geography
Chemistry
Biology
Physics
French
Maths

Please visit www.oakabooks.co.uk for more information about forthcoming titles

© Copyright 2016 Oaka Books. All rights reserved.
Written by Kate Doehren, MA Ed, B.Ed Hons, RSA Dip, Sp LD/Dyslexia
Director of Learning Support, Hurstpierpoint College. Illustrations by Laurence Andrew Page.

First paperback edition printed 2014 in the United Kingdom.
A catalogue record for this book is available from the British Library.

ISBN 978-1-909892-44-6
No part of this book shall be reproduced or transmitted in any form or by any means, electronic or mechanical, including photocopying, recording or by any information retrieval system without written permission of the copyright owner or a licence permitting restricted copying issued by the Copyright Licensing Agency Ltd, Saffron House, 6-10 Kirby Street, London EC1N 8TS Tel: 020 7400 3100   Fax: 020 7400 3101   Email: cla@cla.co.uk   Web: www.cla.co.uk

Designed, set and published by Oaka™ Books.
To order other titles from Oaka™ Books, please email info@oakabooks.co.uk or visit www.oakabooks.co.uk, or phone: +44 (023) 92 388519.

Acknowledgements
Our huge thanks go to the many teachers who have been involved in the development of this series of learning guides. Special thanks to Joy Gardiner, for producing hundreds of illustrations, to Kate Doehren, for her enthusiasm and invaluable assistance to my wonderful daughter Sophie, for being the inspiration for the books and, of course, to Charlie, for believing in them.